Expressions
Fourteen colourful pieces for organ

Dom Andrew Moore

Kevin Mayhew

We hope you enjoy *Expressions*.
Further copies of this and other books in the series are available
from your local music shop or Christian bookshop.

In case of difficulty, please contact the publisher direct by writing to:

The Sales Department
KEVIN MAYHEW LTD
Rattlesden
Bury St Edmunds
Suffolk IP30 0SZ

Phone 0449 737978
Fax 0449 737834

Please ask for our complete catalogue of outstanding Church Music.

Front Cover: *Ode to Music* by John Melhuish Strudwick (1849-1937).
Reproduced by kind permission of Roy Miles Fine Paintings,
London/Bridgeman Art Library, London.

Cover designed by Juliette Clarke and Graham Johnstone
Picture Research: Jane Rayson

First published in Great Britain in 1993 by Kevin Mayhew Ltd

© Copyright 1993 Kevin Mayhew Ltd

ISBN 0 86209 475 5

Music Editor: Joanne Clarke
Music Setting: Kevin Whomes

Contents

	Page
Adagio Dolente	10
Allegro Gioioso	46
Barcarolle	6
Cantabile	4
Fanfare for the Gloria	26
Fantasia on 'Westminster Abbey'	12
In Memoriam	24
Nobilmente	22
Prelude on 'Eventide'	44
Suite	
1. Fanfare - Chorale	29
2. Plaint	32
3. Berceuse	34
4. Toccata	39
Tuba Tune	15

DOM ANDREW MOORE, a Benedictine monk of Downside Abbey near Bath, was born in London in 1954. He studied at the Royal Academy of Music and at Cambridge University. In addition to musical responsibilities at the Abbey as monastic choirmaster he has also been choirmaster for the school, a housemaster and bursar.

CANTABILE

Dom Andrew Moore (*b.* 1954)

Fine

Sw. or Gt.

Man.

D.C. al Fine

BARCAROLLE

Dom Andrew Moore

Poco allegretto ma tranquillo

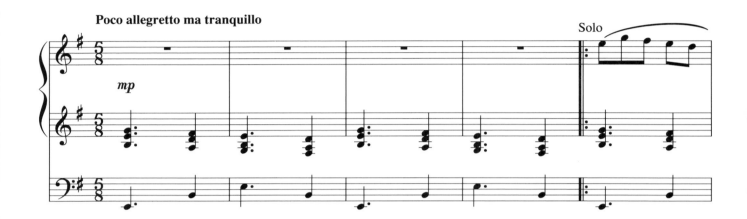

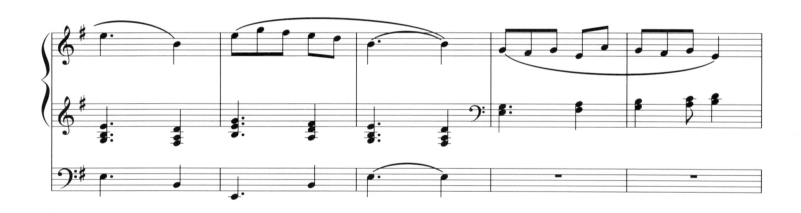

7

9

ADAGIO DOLENTE

Dom Andrew Moore

Fine

Flute

Dal segno al Fine

11

FANTASIA on 'Westminster Abbey'

Dom Andrew Moore

(2nd time rall.)

Fine

Ad lib. Gt.+Ped. *f*
or Sw. senza Ped. *mf*

D.C. al Fine

TUBA TUNE
Dom Andrew Moore

16

18

20

21

for Dom Cyprian Stockford

NOBILMENTE

Dom Andrew Moore

Nobilmente

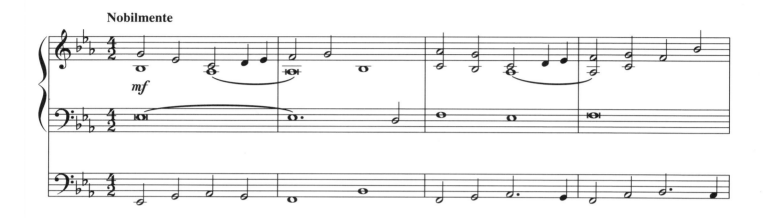

23

for Dom Gregory Murray

IN MEMORIAM

Dom Andrew Moore

FANFARE FOR THE GLORIA

Dom Andrew Moore

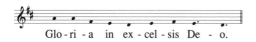

Glo - ri - a in ex - cel - sis De - o.

Andante maestoso

27

Add to Ped.

SUITE
Dom Andrew Moore

1. Fanfare - Chorale

30

2. Plaint

33

3. Berceuse

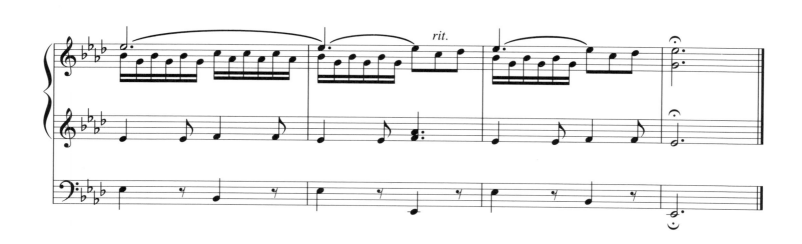

4. Toccata

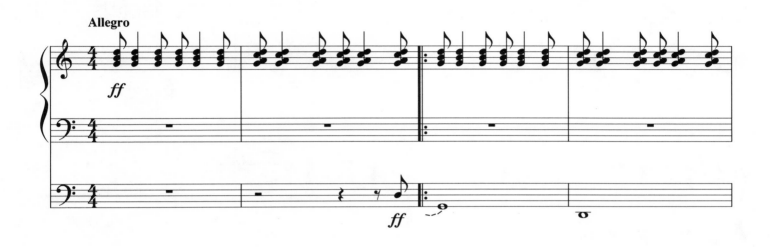

Man.

41

Full Gt.+Sw. *(box closed)*   *poco a poco cresc.*

PRELUDE on 'Eventide'

Dom Andrew Moore

For Peter Matthews

ALLEGRO GIOIOSO

Dom Andrew Moore

48